STUDENT WORKBOOK

Pearson's Anatomy and Physiology for Medical Assisting

VOLUME II

Nina Beaman, MS, RNC, CMA

Bryant and Stratton College
Richmond, VA

PEARSON

Prentice
Hall

Prentice Hall Health
Upper Saddle River, New Jersey 07458

Pearson Prentice Hall™ is a trademark of Pearson Education, Inc.
Pearson® is a registered trademark of Pearson plc.
Prentice Hall® is a registered trademark of Pearson Education, Inc.

Pearson Education Ltd., *London*
Pearson Education Australia Pty. Limited, *Sydney*
Pearson Education Singapore, Pte. Ltd.
Pearson Education North Asia Ltd., *Hong Kong*
Pearson Education Canada, Ltd., *Toronto*
Pearson Educación de Mexico, S.A. de C.V.
Pearson Education—Japan, *Tokyo*
Pearson Education Malaysia, Pte. Ltd.
Pearson Education, Upper Saddle River, New Jersey

10 9 8 7 6 5 4 3 2 1
ISBN 0-13-235103-7

Contents

Chapter **19** Body Structure and Function   162

Chapter **20** The Integumentary System   169

Chapter **21** The Skeletal System   176

Chapter **22** The Muscular System   184

Chapter **23** The Nervous System   190

Chapter **24** The Special Senses   196

Chapter **25** The Circulatory System   204

Chapter **26** The Immune System   213

Chapter **27** The Respiratory System   220

Chapter **28** The Digestive System   227

Chapter **29** The Urinary System   233

Chapter **30** The Endocrine System   239

Chapter **31** The Reproductive System   245

INTRODUCTION

This student workbook is designed to accompany *Pearson's Anatomy and Physiology for Medical Assisting* as a study guide and practice tool. Complete each exercise in the chapters of this workbook as they correspond with chapters of the textbook to help reinforce and supplement what you have learned. Each chapter includes the following:

Chapter Outline: A quick refresher of the topics that were covered in this chapter. If you can't clearly remember one of the topics, it may be a good idea to go back to the book and look over that section.

Medical Terminology Review: Terms from the chapter that can be practiced by using a dictionary and/or in-text definitions.

Chapter Review: A short summary of the chapter. Again, if anything seems unclear, go back to that section in the text.

Study Aids: These questions and small tasks assess whether or not you learned and retained the information in the chapter.

Skill Building: Exercises that allow you to explore possible real-world situations.

Critical Thinking: These questions allow you to apply your knowledge to real-life scenarios.

Chapter Review Test: Multiple choice, True/False and Fill in the Blank quizzes that provide additional practice for the certification exams.

CONTRIBUTOR

Shelly Rainer, LPN
Vatterott College
Springfield, MO

REVIEWERS

Janie Corbitt, RN, BSL
Central Georgia Technical College
Milledgeville, GA

Kendra J. Allen, LPN
Ohio Institute of Health Careers
Columbus, OH

Lisa Nagle, CMA, BSed
Augusta Technical College
Augusta, GA

Amy Knight, CMA
Remington College
New Port Richey, FL

Lory Lee Serrato, CCS-P
Everest College
Springfield, MO

Lisa L. Cook, CMA
Bryman College
Port Orchard, WA

Mary Marks, FNP-C, MSN, Pbt(ASCP)
Mitchell Community College
Mooresville, NC

Nancy H. Wright, RN BS CNOR
Virginia College
Birmingham, Al

Lynn G. Slack, CMA
ICM School of Business and Medical Careers
Pittsburgh, PA

Shirley Jelmo, CMA
Pima Medical Institute
Colorado Springs, CO

CHAPTER 19
Body Structure and Function

CHAPTER OUTLINE

Review the Chapter Outline. If any content area is unclear, review that area before beginning workbook exercises.

    A. The Human Body: Levels of Organization

    B. Anatomical Locations and Positions

    C. Chemistry

    D. Genetics and Heredity

CHAPTER REVIEW

The following is a summary of the chapter. If any of this material is unclear, review it in the textbook again.

Anatomy is the study of the structure of an organism, and physiology is the study of the organism's function. Aging or malfunction of a part of the body can lead to diseases or disorders. The study of diseases and disorders is known as *pathophysiology*.

The body' structure consists of increasingly complex and larger systems: atoms, molecules, cells, tissues, organs, organ systems, and the organism. The body seeks to maintain homeostasis but does respond to internal and external stimuli. Both positive and negative feedback systems cause body responses. Electrolytes, such as sodium, potassium, and chloride, cause changes in the body. Cells divide and reproduce via meiosis or mitosis.

In the anatomic position a person stands upright, with the palms turned forward. Numerous planes hypothetically divide the body into regions. Cavities are hollow spaces within the body that contain either organs, organ systems, or air.

Cells must receive nourishment and eliminate wastes; to do this, transport mechanisms are needed. There are three types of transport: diffusion, osmosis, and filtration. Phagocytosis and pinocytosis are transport media. Genetics is the study of heredity and any variations that occur. When a child is born with a disorder, the disorder is called *congenital*. Congenital disorders include albinism, attention deficit hyperactivity disorder (ADHD), cleft palate, color deficiency, cystic fibrosis, fragile X syndrome, hemochromatosis, hemophilia, Klinefelter's syndrome, muscular dystrophy, phenylketonuria (PKU), sickle cell anemia, spina bifida, Turner's syndrome, and talipes.

162

STUDY AIDS

To ensure that you have achieved the learning objectives:

1. Spell and define the Terms to Learn in the chapter.

2. Create a chart listing the systems of the body, the organs in each system, and the function of each organ.

3. Define the terms used to describe the directions, planes, and cavities of the body.

_____

_____

_____

_____

_____

_____

_____

MEDICAL TERMINOLOGY REVIEW

Using a dictionary and highlighted terms in the textbook, define the following terms.

Active transport _____

_____

Anatomic position _____

_____

Anatomy _____

_____

Atom _____

_____

Cavities _____

● _____

Cell _____

_____

Cell membrane _____

_____

Cilia _____

_____

Cytokinesis _____

_____

Cytoplasm _____

_____

Diaphragm _____

_____

DNA (deoxyribonucleic acid) _____

_____

Electrolyte _____

_____

Genetics _____

_____

● meostasis _____

_____

Lysosomes _____

_____

Meiosis _____

_____

Mitochondrion _____

_____

Mitosis _____

_____

Molecule _____

_____

Nucleus _____

_____

Organelles _____

_____

Organs _____

_____

Passive transport _____

● _____

Pathophysiology _____

_____

Physiology _____

_____

Ribosome _____

_____

RNA (ribonucleic acid) _____

_____

Selective permeability _____

_____

System _____

_____

Tissue _____

_____

SKILL BUILDING

Read and follow the directions below.

1. Create a book of diagrams of humans in the anatomic position. Label the directions, planes, and cavities of the body.

2. Make an "edible cell." You could, for example, bake a cake representing cytoplasm and decorate it with candies for the different organelles.

CRITICAL THINKING

1. Discuss how a small town is similar to a cell. For example, the nucleus is like city hall and the DNA is stored in the town library.

   _____

   _____

   _____

   _____

2. Read the Case Study described at the beginning of the chapter. Should a medical assistant describe the location of the pain or note the patient's opinion of its origin?

   _____

   _____

   _____

   _____

3. Describe why many disorders occur only in males.

   _____

   _____

   _____

   _____

CHAPTER REVIEW TEST

MULTIPLE CHOICE

Circle the letter of the correct answer.

1. What word should you use to describe the liver?
   a. gluteal
   b. popliteal
   c. hepatic
   d. lumbar
   e. patellar

2. What word should you use to describe the area behind the knee?
   a. gluteal
   b. popliteal
   c. hepatic
   d. lumbar
   e. patellar

3. In which system is the skin found?
   a. digestive
   b. endocrine
   c. integumentary
   d. muscular
   e. nervous

4. Which word describes the study of the function of an organism?
   a. histology
   b. anatomy
   c. physiology
   d. pathophysiology
   e. biology

5. When all systems work together to balance the organism, the condition is known as
   a. hemostasis
   b. homeostasis
   c. histology
   d. mitochondria
   e. molecule

6. The smallest living units are
   a. atoms
   b. molecules
   c. cells
   d. tissues
   e. organs

7. The work area of the cell is known as the
   a. cell membrane
   b. cytoplasm
   c. Golgi apparatus
   d. centrioles
   e. endoplasmic reticulum

8. A network of tubules in the cell is the
   a. cell membrane
   b. cytoplasm
   c. Golgi apparatus
   d. centrioles
   e. endoplasmic reticulum

9. Prior to separation, chromosomes are arranged in a cluster. This phase is called
   a. prophase
   b. metaphase
   c. anaphase
   d. telophase

10. The word meaning "toward the head" is
    a. anterior
    b. posterior
    c. superior
    d. inferior
    e. caudal

TRUE/FALSE

Indicate whether the statement is true (T) or false (F).

_____ 1. The study of an organism's function is anatomy.

_____ 2. Pathophysiology is the study of diseases and disorders.

_____ 3. Sodium, chloride, and potassium are examples of electrolytes.

_____ 4. Standing upright with the arm extended is the anatomic position.

_____ 5. The body's hollow spaces are referred to as *cavities* and may contain air, organs, or organ systems.

_____ 6. Transport mechanisms nourish cells and eliminate waste.

_____ 7. Filtration, osmosis, and infusion are types of transport mechanisms.

_____ 8. The study of heredity is termed *genetics*.

_____ 9. ADHD is not considered a congenital disorder.

_____ 10. *Popliteal* refers to the knee.

FILL IN THE BLANK

Using words from the list below, fill in the blanks to complete the following statements.

mitosis	connective
structure	muscular
phagocytosis	nerve
endocrine	diseases
abdominopelvic	disorders
epithelical	organs

1. The _____ system includes the thyroid.

2. The _____ of an organism is its anatomy.

3. _____ and _____ result from aging and body system disorders.

4. _____ occurs when cells divide rapidly.

5. Transport media consist of pinocytosis and _____.

6. Atoms, molecules, cells, tissues, _____, and systems make up the human body.

7. The dorsal, ventral, and _____ areas are the anatomic cavities.

8. Our bodies have four types of tissue: _____, _____, _____, and _____.

CHAPTER 20
The Integumentary System

CHAPTER OUTLINE

Review the Chapter Outline. If any content area is unclear, review that area before beginning workbook exercises.

    A.   Overview of the Integumentary System

    B.   Functions of the Integumentary System

    C.   Layers of the Skin

    D.   Accessory Structures of the Skin

    E.   Common Disorders Associated with the Integumentary System

CHAPTER REVIEW

The following is a summary of the chapter. If any of this material is unclear, review it in the textbook again.

The skin is part of the integumentary system and is the largest organ in the body. The integumentary system has multiple roles in homeostasis, including protection, temperature regulation, sensory reception, and secretion. The skin consists of two layers. The epidermis is the upper layer, comprised of four strata. Under the epidermis is the dermis. Accessory organs include nails, hair, sweat glands, and sebaceous glands.

Many problems can occur in the integumentary system. Cancers such as squamous cell carcinomas and melanomas can grow and spread. Acne vulgaris is caused by inflamed and infected sebaceous glands. Alopecia is hair loss, and cellulitis is an infection in the cells. Contact dermatitis occurs when the skin reacts to a stimulus. Eczema is dry, weeping skin. Folliculitis occurs when the hair follicle becomes inflamed. Herpes simplex and herpes zoster are viruses. Impetigo is highly contagious. Pediculosis is lice infestation. Psoriasis is a scaly, dry skin condition. Rosacea produces red skin. Scabies are tiny creatures that infest the skin. Warts are also caused by viruses. Burns cause trauma to the skin.

STUDY AIDS

To ensure that you have achieved the learning objectives:

1.   Define and spell the Terms to Learn in the chapter.

_____

_____

_____

_____

_____

_____

_____

_____

_____

_____

_____

_____

_____

_____

_____

_____

_____

_____

_____

_____

2. Create a chart of the accessory structures of the integumentary system.

3. List the functions of the skin.

_____

_____

_____

_____

_____

_____

_____

_____

_____

_____

4. Explain how the skin of a child and of an older adult differ.
5. Create a chart of the common disorders of the integumentary system.

MEDICAL TERMINOLOGY REVIEW

Using a dictionary and highlighted terms in the textbook, define the following terms.

Acne vulgaris _____

_____

Alopecia _____

_____

Cellulitis _____

Contact dermatitis _____

Decubitus ulcer _____

Dermis _____

Eczema _____

Epidermis _____

Folliculitis _____

Herpes simplex _____

Herpes zoster _____

Impetigo _____

Malignant melanoma _____

Pediculosis _____

Psoriasis _____

Rosacea _____

Scabies _____

Sebaceous glands _____

Squamous cell carcinoma _____

Sudoriferous glands _____

Sweat glands _____

Wart _____

SKILL BUILDING

Read and follow the directions below.

List and describe laboratory tests related to the integumentary system.

CRITICAL THINKING

1. A patient comes in with a rash that you do not recognize but that you think might be eczema. What do you say to the patient?

_____

_____

_____

2. A patient calls and describes a third-degree burn. Do you tell the patient to come to the office or go to the emergency department of a hospital?

_____

_____

_____

3. A patient comes in with itch mites. How can you prevent the mites from transferring to you or to other patients who enter the room later?

_____

_____

_____

_____

CHAPTER REVIEW TEST

MULTIPLE CHOICE

Circle the letter of the correct answer.

1. Which of the following means a blister or an open sore on the skin? The area around the site may be red and irritated.
   a. stage I pressure ulcer
   b. stage II pressure ulcer
   c. stage III pressure ulcer
   d. stage IV pressure ulcer

2. Which of the following consists of dead or dying tissue?
   a. stratum corneum
   b. stratum lucidum
   c. stratum granulosum
   d. stratum germinativum

3. Which of the following regenerates tissue?
   a. stratum corneum
   b. stratum lucidum
   c. stratum granulosum
   d. stratum germinativum

4. Which of the following is caused by an itch mite?
   a. herpes
   b. pediculosis
   c. scabies
   d. impetigo
   e. cancer

5. Which of the following is a form of skin cancer?
   a. eczema
   b. psoriasis
   c. melanoma
   d. pediculosis
   e. impetigo

6. Which of the following is a virus?
   a. pediculosis
   b. scabies
   c. eczema
   d. herpes
   e. psoriasis

7. Which of the following causes reddened skin?
   a. alopecia
   b. rosacea
   c. impetigo
   d. melanoma
   e. pediculosis

8. Which of the following is caused by infected sebaceous glands?
   a. pediculosis
   b. acne vulgaris
   c. folliculitis
   d. cellulitis
   e. rosacea

9. Which of the following means hair loss?
   a. folliculitis
   b. cellulitis
   c. alopecia
   d. rosacea
   e. pediculosis

10. Which of the following is NOT caused by a virus?
    a. herpes simplex
    b. herpes zoster
    c. pediculosis
    d. wart
    e. chicken pox

TRUE/FALSE

Indicate whether the statement is true (T) or false (F).

_____ 1. The body's largest organ is the skin.

_____ 2. The dermis and the epidermis are the two layers of skin.

_____ 3. Sweat glands, hair, and callouses are all accessory organs.

_____ 4. Melanomas, found on the skin, can grow and spread.

_____ 5. Infected sebaceous glands are known as *acne vulgaris*.

_____ 6. When the skin experiences a reaction to a stimulus, contact dermatitis occurs.

_____ 7. Herpes simplex is a virus that produces cold sores.

_____ 8. Pediculosis is a scabies infection.

_____ 9. Pressure ulcers are classified in stages I, II, III, and IV.

_____ 10. Hair loss is referred to as _alopecia_.

FILL IN THE BLANK

Using words from the list below, fill in the blanks to complete the following statements.

analysis	cellulitus
hair	excretory
eczema	vasodilation
scabies	sweat glands
upper	athlete's foot
dermatitis	

1. The _____ layer of the skin is the epidermis.

2. Sebaceous glands are _____ organs.

3. Often weeping, dry skin is _____.

4. The itch mite causes _____, a highly contagious disorder.

5. Inflammation of connective or cellular tissues is _____.

6. Temperature regulation is accomplished by _____.

7. Water is excreted onto the skin's surface by the _____.

8. _____ of a _____ sample can reveal what was ingested and how long ago.

9. _____ can be described as fissures that extend through the dermis and into the epidermis.

10. Touching poison oak or poison ivy can lead to the condition referred to as _____.

CHAPTER 21
The Skeletal System

CHAPTER OUTLINE

Review the Chapter Outline. If any content area is unclear, review that area before beginning workbook exercises.

A. Bones and Their Classification

B. Joints and Movement

C. The Axial Skeleton

D. The Appendicular Skeleton

E. Common Disorders Associated with the Skeletal System

CHAPTER REVIEW

The following is a summary of the chapter. If any of this material is unclear, review it in the textbook again.

The skeletal system provides support, storage of bone marrow, and movement. Bones are named by their function, location, or shape. Joints allow for movement. The axial skeleton consists of all parts of the skeleton other than the arms and legs. The appendicular skeleton comprises the arms and legs. This very important system can have abnormalities and diseases. Some of those covered in this chapter are lordosis, scoliosis, kyphosis, arthritis, carpal tunnel syndrome, gout, bursitis, fractures, and dislocations.

STUDY AIDS

To ensure that you have achieved the learning objectives:

1. Define and spell the Terms to Learn in the chapter.

_____

_____

_____

_____

_____

_____

_____

_____

_____

_____

_____

_____

_____

_____

_____

_____

_____

_____

_____

_____

_____

_____

_____

_____

_____

_____

_____

_____

_____

_____

_____

2. Draw and label the skeletal system of the body.

3. Explain various types of body movement.
4. Discuss the vertebral column and explain its function.
5. Identify three abnormal curvatures of the spine.

_____

_____

_____

6. Discuss the male and female pelvis and explain the differences between them.
7. List and explain 10 common disorders of the skeletal system.

_____

_____

_____

_____

_____

_____

_____

_____

_____

_____

8. Create a chart to identify various types of fractures.

MEDICAL TERMINOLOGY REVIEW

Using a dictionary and highlighted terms in the textbook, define the following terms.

Abduction _____

_____

Adduction _____

_____

Amphiarthrotic joint _____

_____

Appendicular skeleton _____

_____

Arthritis _____

_____

Articulation _____

_____

Axial skeleton _____

_____

Bursitis _____

_____

Cancellous (spongy) bone _____

_____

Circumduction _____

_____

Compact bone _____

_____

Diaphysis _____

_____

Diarthrotic joint _____

_____

Dislocation _____

_____

Dorsiflexion _____

_____

Endosteum _____

_____

Epiphysis _____

_____

Eversion _____

_____

Extension _____

_____

Flexion _____

_____

Gout _____

_____

Inversion _____

_____

Medullary canal _____

_____

Osteoarthritis _____

_____

Osteoporosis _____

_____

Periosteum _____

_____

Pronation _____

_____

Protraction _____

_____

Retraction _____

_____

Rheumatoid arthritis _____

_____

Rotation _____

_____

Supination _____

_____

Synarthrotic joint _____

_____

SKILL BUILDING

Read and follow the directions below.

Draw a picture of a skeleton and label the parts.

CRITICAL THINKING

1. If a patient presents with a dislocated arm, should you try to return it to its normal location or splint it in the position found?

    _____

    _____

    _____

    _____

2. Why is the outlet of the female pelvis wider than that of the male pelvis?

    _____

    _____

    _____

    _____

3. Why is it important to eat dairy products and get some exposure to the sun?

    _____

    _____

    _____

    _____

CHAPTER REVIEW TEST

MULTIPLE CHOICE

Circle the letter of the correct answer.

1. Which of the following means a fracture that frequently results from reaching forward to stop or cushion a fall? This fracture is exemplified by a break in the distal portion of the radius.
   a. comminuted
   b. Colles'
   c. open
   d. closed
   e. greenstick

2. Which of the following fractures is frequently found in children, whose bones bend rather than break?
   a. comminuted
   b. Colles'
   c. open
   d. closed
   e. greenstick

3. Which of the following is caused by repetitive stress in the wrist?
   a. osteoporosis
   b. osteoarthritis
   c. carpal tunnel syndrome
   d. gout
   e. bursitis

4. Which of the following is part of the appendicular skeleton?
   a. torso
   b. neck
   c. head
   d. arm

5. Which of the following is caused by a buildup of uric acid?
   a. osteoporosis
   b. osteoarthritis
   c. carpal tunnel syndrome
   d. gout
   e. bursitis

6. Which of the following is part of the axial skeleton?
   a. wrist
   b. elbow
   c. head
   d. knee
   e. foot

7. Which of the following means a bone fracture that breaks the skin?
   a. Colles'
   b. carpal tunnel syndrome
   c. greenstick
   d. open
   e. closed

8. Hemopoiesis occurs in the
   a. wrists
   b. bone marrow
   c. toes
   d. liver
   e. vertebrae

9. Which of the following describes toes turned outward?
   a. inversion
   b. eversion
   c. dorsiflexion
   d. plantar flexion
   e. abduction

10. Which of the following describes movement away from the body?
    a. adduction
    b. abduction
    c. circumduction
    d. flexion
    e. eversion

TRUE/FALSE

Indicate whether the statement is true (T) or false (F).

_____ 1. Bone types are classified by their shape: long, short, flat, and round.

_____ 2. The hollow region that acts as a storage area for bone marrow is called the *medullary cavity*.

_____ 3. Tightly packed, dense, hard tissue composing the shafts of long bones and the outer layers of other bones is known as *compact bone*.

_____ 4. Endosteum serves two purposes; it provides a space for red bone marrow and it provides nutrients.

_____ 5. Bones' grooves and depressions act as pathways for nerves and blood vessels.

_____ 6. Longitudinal bone growth can support body weight more efficiently.

_____ 7. Formation and growth of bone involve five types of cells.

_____ 8. The bursa contains a lubricant called *synovial fluid*.

_____ 9. An example of a fibrous joint is the sutures in the skull.

_____ 10. A bone cannot be flat and long.

FILL IN THE BLANK

Using words from the list below, fill in the blanks to complete the following statements.

cervical region	compound
slide	xiphoid
ossification	pelvic bones
bony plates	

1. Formation of bone in the body is _____ or osteogenesis.

2. Guilding joints _____ back and forth.

3. The skull's _____ are held together with suture lines.

4. Three distinct areas of the sternum are the manubrium, body, and _____.

5. Vertebrae numbered C-3 are found in the _____.

6. The gender of a skeleton can be identified by examining the _____.

7. _____ fractures are breaks that expose the bone.

CHAPTER 22
The Muscular System

CHAPTER OUTLINE

Review the Chapter Outline. If any content area is unclear, review that area before beginning workbook exercises.

    A.   Functions of Muscle

    B.   Types of Muscle Tissue

    C.   Energy Production for Muscle

    D.   Structure of Skeletal Muscles

    E.   Major Skeletal Muscles

    F.   Common Disorders Associated with the Muscular System

CHAPTER REVIEW

The following is a summary of the chapter. If any of this material is unclear, review it in the textbook again.

The muscular system is composed of specialized cells called *muscle fibers*. These fibers, which have different lengths, shapes and colors ranging from white to deep red, form and become muscles. Muscles make up about 42 percent of a person's total weight. Each muscle consists of a group of fibers connected by connective tissue held together by a fibrous sheath called *fascia*. Each fiber within a muscle also has its own nervous system connection with a stored supply of energy in the form of glycogen. Muscle must be supplied with proper nutrition and oxygen to perform properly. Muscles are named by their location and function. They need energy to contract, and overuse of muscles can lead to fatigue. Muscular dystrophy and myasthenia gravis weaken and affect the activity of muscles. Fibromyalgia is a chronic pain disorder of the muscles. Muscles that are not used and exercised can atrophy. Injuries can cause tendonitis, sprains, strains, and pain. Pain can also be caused by muscle cramps. Tetanus can severely impair muscle function.

STUDY AIDS

To ensure that you have achieved the learning objectives:

1. Define and spell the Terms to Learn in the chapter.

_____

_____

_____

_____

_____

_____

_____
_____
_____
_____
_____
_____
_____
_____
_____
_____
_____
_____
_____
_____
_____
_____
_____
_____

2. Describe the muscular system of the body.

3. Explain the functions of muscle.

   Identify and discuss the various types of muscle tissue.

5. Explain the structure of skeletal muscles.

6. Discuss attachments to skeletal muscles.

7. Identify the major muscles of the body.

8. Identify and explain common disorders of the muscular system.

MEDICAL TERMINOLOGY REVIEW

Using a dictionary and highlighted terms in the textbook, define the following terms.

Antagonist _____

_____

Aponeurosis _____

_____

Atrophy _____

_____

Cardiac muscle _____

_____

Endomysium _____

_____

Epimysium _____

_____

Fascia _____

_____

Fascicles _____

_____

Fibromyalgia _____

_____

Insertion _____

_____

Muscle cramps _____

_____

Muscular dystrophy (MD) _____

_____

Myasthenia gravis (MG) _____

_____

Origin _____

_____

Oxygen debt _____

_____

Perimysium _____

_____

Prime mover _____

_____

Skeletal muscle _____

_____

Smooth muscle _____

_____

Sprain _____

_____

Strain _____

_____

Synergist _____

_____

Tendonitis _____

_____

Tendons _____

_____

Tetanus _____

_____

SKILL BUILDING

Read and follow the directions below.

1. Role play with a colleague caring for a patient with muscle atrophy or pain in the medical office.
2. If a patient presented with muscle injury, describe what you would do.

CRITICAL THINKING

1. Why is it important to get tetanus vaccinations? What can happen to patients who are not vaccinated?

_____

_____

_____

_____

2. Is fibromyalgia real or do patients just make it up to get attention?

_____

_____

_____

Why do muscles fatigue if overused?

_____

_____

_____

_____

CHAPTER REVIEW TEST

MULTIPLE CHOICE

Circle the letter of the correct answer.

1. Which of the following is voluntary skeletal muscle?
   a. cardiac
   b. smooth
   c. striated

2. A group of fibrous tissues is known as
   a. fibromyalgia
   b. dystrophy
   c. atrophy
   d. fascia
   e. tetanus

3. Which of the following means an inflammation of the tendon?
   a. tetanus
   b. tetany
   c. tendonitis
   d. tonicity

4. What percentage of body weight is usually muscle?
   a. 10–20
   b. 20–30
   c. 30–40
   d. 40–50
   e. 50–60

5. Which is a wide, thin, sheet-like tendon?
   a. fascia
   b. aponeurosis
   c. atrophy
   d. antagonist
   e. insertion

6. Which of the following is a fixed attachment to a bone?
   a. insertion
   b. origin
   c. aponeurosis
   d. perimysium
   e. synergist

7. Splenus capitis is found in the
   a. neck
   b. head
   c. chest
   d. abdomen
   e. foot

8. Pectoralis major is found in the
   a. neck
   b. head
   c. chest
   d. abdomen
   e. foot

9. Gastrocnemius is found in the
   a. neck
   b. head
   c. chest
   d. leg
   e. foot

10. A muscle that counteracts, or opposes, the action of another muscle is called a(n)
   a. aponeurosis
   b. antagonist
   c. prime mover
   d. synergist
   e. fascia

TRUE/FALSE

Indicate whether the statement is true (T) or false (F).

_____ 1. The skeletal muscles allow us to perform external movements.

_____ 2. Peristalsis is performed by the smooth visceral muscle.

_____ 3. Cardiac muscle is always under conscious control.

_____ 4. Contraction and reflection coordinate to give the body movement.

_____ 5. Providing both voluntary and involuntary control, the diaphragm brings air into the lungs.

_____ 6. All muscles are voluntary.

_____ 7. Kicking a soccer ball requires both extensor and flexor muscles.

_____ 8. Most skeletal muscles are involuntary.

_____ 9. Lack of coordination is a condition called *spasm*.

_____ 10. Protrusion of an organ through a tear in the muscle wall is a hernia.

FILL IN THE BLANK

Using words from the list below, fill in the blanks to complete the following statements.

skeletal muscles	rigor mortis
flaccid	vasoconstriction
extension	point of insertion
sarcoplasmic reticulum	shivering
myasthenia gravis	trapezius

1. Found in the shoulder is the _____ muscle.

2. _____ describes the muscle end that is attached to the moving bone.

3. *Rotation, abduction, adduction,* _____, and flexion are terms used to describe the direction of body movements.

4. A specialized series of interconnecting tubules and sacs that surround each myofibril is called _____.

5. _____ is the stiffening process of the body after death.

6. Increased blood pressure due to smooth muscle contractions that restrict the blood vessel is called _____.

7. Stimulated _____ are able to contract 50 times faster than smooth muscle.

8. _____ describes unused muscles that lose their tone.

9. _____ is the body's way of generating heat through muscle contractions.

10. Drooping of one or both eyes and gradual, profound muscle weakness are symptoms of _____.

CHAPTER 23
The Nervous System

CHAPTER OUTLINE

Review the Chapter Outline. If any content area is unclear, review that area before beginning workbook exercises.

A. Functions of the Nervous System

B. Neurons

C. Nerve Fiber, Nerves, and Tracts

D. Nerve Impulses and Synapses

E. Central Nervous System

F. Peripheral Nervous System

G. Autonomic Nervous System

H. Common Disorders Associated with the Nervous System

CHAPTER REVIEW

The following is a summary of the chapter. If any of this material is unclear, review it in the textbook again.

The nervous system is the body's information gatherer, storage center, and control system. Its overall function is to collect information about the external conditions in relation to the body's external state, to analyze this information, and to initiate appropriate responses to satisfy certain needs. The most powerful of these needs is survival. The nerves do not form a single system, but rather several interrelated ones. Some of these systems are physically separate; others are different in function only. The brain and spinal cord make up the central nervous system. The peripheral nervous system is responsible for the body's functions that are not under conscious control—like the heartbeat or the digestive system. The smooth operation of the peripheral nervous system is achieved by dividing it into sympathetic and parasympathetic systems. These are opposing systems and check each other to provide balance. The nervous system uses electrical impulses, which travel along the length of the cells. The cell processes information from the sensory nerves and initiates action within milliseconds. These impulses travel at a rate of up to 250 miles per hour, while other systems, such as the endocrine system, may take many hours to respond by releasing hormones.

The nervous system is responsible for three separate functions. It detects and interprets sensory information. It then takes that information and makes decisions about how it is being received. And finally, it carries out a function based upon the decisions made.

Nerve fibers make up tracts that carry impulses across synapses. The central nervous system is comprised of the brain and spinal cord. The cerebrum, the largest part of the brain, is divided into lobes. Specific functions occur in different parts of the cerebrum. The diencephalon, midbrain, and hindbrain control body functions.

Cerebrospinal fluid bathes the brain and spinal cord. The peripheral nervous system is composed of cranial and spinal nerves. The sympathetic nervous system reacts to the environment, and the parasympathetic nervous system relaxes to a normal level. These two systems make up the autonomic nervous system. Some common disorders associated with the nervous system are Alzheimer's disease, amyotrophic lateral sclerosis (ALS), Bell's palsy, encephalitis, epilepsy and seizure disorders, headaches, meningitis, multiple sclerosis (MS), neuralgia, paraplegia, quadriplegia, Parkinson's disease. sciatica, spina bifida, and stroke.

STUDY AIDS

To ensure that you have achieved the learning objectives:

1. Define and spell the Terms to Learn in the chapter.

_____
_____
_____
_____
_____
_____
_____
_____
_____
_____
_____
_____
_____
_____
_____
_____
_____
_____
_____

2. Identify and discuss the structures that make up the nervous system.
3. Explain how nerve impulses are transmitted.
4. State the functions of the central nervous system, the peripheral nervous system, and the autonomic nervous system and discuss the differences between them.
5. Identify and explain the common disorders of the nervous system.

MEDICAL TERMINOLOGY REVIEW

Using a dictionary and highlighted terms in the textbook, define the following terms.

Alzheimer's disease _____

_____

Amyotrophic lateral sclerosis (ALS) _____

_____

Bell's palsy _____

_____

Cerebrospinal fluid _____

_____

Encephalitis _____

_____

Epilepsy _____

_____

Headache _____

_____

Meningitis _____

_____

Multiple sclerosis (MS) _____

_____

Neuralgia _____

_____

Paraplegia _____

_____

Parkinson's disease _____

_____

Quadriplegia _____

_____

Sciatica _____

_____

Seizure _____

_____

Spina bifida _____

_____

Stroke _____

_____

SKILL BUILDING

Read and follow the directions below.

1. Role play how you would treat a patient with a headache.
2. Role play how you would take vital signs on a patient with a traumatic brain injury.

CRITICAL THINKING

1. Why does your mouth feel dry when you are nervous?

   _____

   _____

   _____

   _____

2. Why do patients tend to urinate during seizures?

   _____

   _____

   _____

   _____

3. Why do patients with amyotrophic lateral sclerosis have trouble with physical movement?

   _____

   _____

   _____

   _____

4. Your patient has Alzheimer's disease. How might that change your management of his appointment in the office?

   _____

   _____

   _____

   _____

CHAPTER REVIEW TEST

MULTIPLE CHOICE

Circle the letter of the correct answer.

1. In which of the following conditions are all limbs paralyzed?
   a. paraplegia
   b. quadriplegia
   c. sciatica
   d. neuralgia
   e. Parkinson's disease

2. Which of the following causes loss of memory?
   a. Alzheimer's disease
   b. Amyotrophic lateral sclerosis
   c. Parkinson's disease
   d. Bell's palsy
   e. multiple sclerosis

3. Which of the following primarily affects the cranial nerves?
   a. Alzheimer's disease
   b. amyotrophic lateral sclerosis
   c. Parkinson's disease
   d. Bell's palsy
   e. multiple sclerosis

4. Which organ controls breathing?
   a. cerebrum
   b. hypothalamus
   c. medulla oblongata
   d. pons
   e. corpus callosum

5. Which organ is located in the diencephalon?
   a. cerebrum
   b. cerebellum
   c. hypothalamus
   d. corpus callosum
   e. pons

6. Which of the following causes seizures?
   a. Bell's palsy
   b. quadriplegia
   c. spina bifida
   d. epilepsy
   e. Alzheimer's disease

7. In which of the following conditions is the spinal tissue located outside of the body?
   a. Parkinson's disease
   b. amyotrophic lateral sclerosis
   c. spina bifida
   d. epilepsy
   e. Bell's palsy

8. Which of the following causes leg pain?
   a. spina bifida
   b. multiple sclerosis
   c. sciatica
   d. Bell's palsy
   e. Parkinson's disease

9. Which of the following headaches are usually unilateral?
   a. cluster
   b. tension
   c. migraine
   d. posttraumatic

10. Which of the following means infection of the meninges?
    a. sciatica
    b. stroke
    c. meningitis
    d. Alzheimer's disease
    e. Parkinson's disease

TRUE/FALSE

Indicate whether the statement is true (T) or false (F).

_____ 1. The spinal cord and brain comprise the nervous system.

_____ 2. The autonomic nervous system provides a compete network of motor and sensory fibers.

_____ 3. Not under conscious control, output of the autonomic nervous system is involuntary.

_____ 4. The nervous system is always active.

_____ 5. Neurons and neuroglia are found in the connective tissue.

_____ 6. Sensory neurons are input neurons and are classified by function.

_____ 7. The parasympathetic and sympathetic nervous systems provide balance for smooth operation of the peripheral nervous system.

_____ 8. Chemical synapses have special connections called *gap junctions*.

_____ 9. Acetylcholinesterase is the enzyme responsible for cleaning the neuromuscular junction.

FILL IN THE BLANK

Using words from the list below, fill in the blanks to complete the following statements.

corticospinal	spinal cord
corticobulbar	lateral
olfactory	hematoma
reflex	carniosucural
gray matter	frontal lobe
31	autonomic system

1. Divided into _____ segments, with pairs of spinal nerves, located in a hollow tube, is the _____.

2. The dorsal horn, the ventral horn, and the _____ horn are found in the spinal column.

3. Motor output in its simplest form, _____, can occur without the brain's involvement.

4. White matter surrounds _____ in the spinal cord.

5. The sense of smell is produced by the _____ nerve.

6. The premotor and prefrontal areas of the _____ plan movements.

7. Direct pathways from your motor cortex are _____ and _____ tracts.

8. Physiological characteristics like heart rate and digestion are controlled by the _____.

9. _____ describes the neurons of the parasympathetic system.

10. Head injury causing bleeding in the subdural space is called a subderal _____.

CHAPTER 24
The Special Senses

CHAPTER OUTLINE

Review the Chapter Outline. If any content area is unclear, review that area before beginning workbook exercises.

    A. The Eye and the Sense of Vision

    B. The Ear and the Sense of Hearing

    C. The Senses of Taste and Smell

    D. The Sense of Touch

CHAPTER REVIEW

The following is a summary of the chapter. If any of this material is unclear, review it in the textbook again.

The body receives stimuli from the enviroment and relays information to the brain. Eyes provide the sense of vision. Ears provide the sense of hearing. The nose provides the sense of smell, and taste buds are for sensing taste.

The eye has three layers, which work together to place an image in the back of the eye to be sent to the brain.

Common disorders of the eye include refractive errors, age-related disorders, and infections. Refractive errors included hyperopia, presbyopia, and myopia. Strabismus, or crossed eyes, is another common disorder. Astigmatism is caused by an irregular cornea, and amblyopia means the use of only one eye. A cataract is a clouding of the lens. Conjunctivitis is an inflammation of the conjunctiva. Glaucoma is caused by increased pressure building up in the eye. The retina can detach from the back of the eye, and the macula can degenerate over time. The cornea can become scratched or abraded. Hordeolums, or "stys," are very common and contagious.

The ear senses hearing and provides equilibrium. As air moves through the outer, middle, and inner ears, sound is perceived. Otitis media is a very common middle ear disorder. Otosclerosis occurs when the tissue surrounding the bone of the stapes grows abnormally around it. Ménière's disease causes vertigo, fluctuating hearing loss, and a sensation of pressure or pain in the affected ear. Presbycusis is a gradual deterioration of the sensory receptors. Tinnitus, ringing in the ears, is a symptom of many health problems. Cerumen, or ear wax, can become impacted. Audiology is the study of hearing disorders.

The tongue is the organ of taste. Together with the sense of small, the sense of taste helps the body to stimulate taste buds on the tongue.

The sense of touch is the most primitive and pervasive sense. The dermis, when touched, carries much information to the brain. Some areas of the body are more sensitive than others.

STUDY AIDS

To ensure that you have achieved the learning objectives:

1. Define and spell the Terms to Learn in the chapter.

_____

_____

_____

_____

_____

_____

_____

_____

_____

_____

_____

_____

_____

_____

_____

_____

_____

_____

_____

_____

_____

_____

2. List the structures that make up the eye.

_____

_____

_____

_____

_____

3. Explain the function of each structure listed in No. 2 above.

_____

_____

_____

_____

_____

_____

4. List and define common disorders of the eye.

_____

_____

_____

_____

_____

5. List the structures of the ear.

_____

_____

_____

_____

_____

6. Explain the function of each structure listed in No. 5 above.

_____

_____

_____

_____

_____

7. List and define the common disorders of the ear.

_____

_____

_____

_____

_____

8. List the structures of the nose.

_____

_____

_____

_____

_____

9. Explain the function of each structure listed in No. 8 on page 198.

_____
_____
_____
_____
_____
_____

10. List and define the common disorders of the nose.

_____
_____
_____
_____
_____
_____

11. Discuss the sense of taste and briefly explain the function of the taste buds.

MEDICAL TERMINOLOGY REVIEW

Using a dictionary and highlighted terms in the textbook, define the following terms.

Amblyopia _____

Astigmatism _____

Audiology _____

Cataract _____

Conjunctivitis _____

Corneal abrasion _____

Glaucoma _____

Hearing loss _____

Hordeolum _____

Hyperopia _____

_____

Impacted cerumen _____

_____

Macular degeneration _____

_____

Ménière's disease _____

_____

Otitis media _____

_____

Otosclerosis _____

_____

Presbycusis _____

_____

Presbyopia _____

_____

Retinal detachment _____

_____

Strabismus _____

_____

Tinnitus _____

_____

SKILL BUILDING

Read and follow the directions below.

1. Draw a sketch of the eye and label the parts. Then define the purpose of each part.

2. Draw a sketch of the ear and label the parts. Then define the purpose of each part.

CRITICAL THINKING

1. Read the Case Study at the beginning of the chapter. Describe Desiree's pathology. How do you think this two-year-old developed this illness?

_____

_____

_____

_____

2. Procure foods that taste salty, sweet, and bitter. Determine by putting them on your tongue where each sensation is tasted.

_____

_____

_____

_____

CHAPTER REVIEW TEST

MULTIPLE CHOICE

Circle the letter of the correct answer.

1. Which of the following describes the study of hearing and hearing disorders?
   - a. otology
   - b. audiology
   - c. biology
   - d. ophthalmology
   - e. rhinology

2. Which of the following is also known as "pink eye?"
   - a. conjunctivitis
   - b. hordeolum
   - c. tinnitus
   - d. glaucoma
   - e. retinal detachment

3. Which of the following is known as "ringing in the ear?"
   - a. conjunctivitis
   - b. hordeolum
   - c. tinnitus
   - d. glaucoma
   - e. retinal detachment

4. Which of the following is a sty?
   - a. conjunctivitis
   - b. hordeolum
   - c. tinnitus
   - d. glaucoma
   - e. retinal detachment

5. Where is the aqueous humor located?
   - a. anterior part of the eye
   - b. posterior part of the eye
   - c. inner ear
   - d. middle ear
   - e. outer ear

6. The retina is found in the
   - a. outer ear
   - b. middle ear
   - c. inner ear
   - d. anterior part of the eye
   - e. posterior part of the eye

7. Which of the following is also known as "lazy eye?"
   - a. astigmatism
   - b. amblyopia
   - c. myopia
   - d. hyperopia
   - e. presbyopia

8. Which of the following is known as *farsightedness*?
   - a. astigmatism
   - b. amblyopia
   - c. myopia
   - d. hyperopia
   - e. presbyopia

9. Which of the following is hearing loss involving the gradual deterioration of the sensory receptors in the cochlea?
   a. Ménière's disease
   b. otitis media
   c. presbyopia
   d. presbycusis
   e. tinnitus

10. Which taste is located on the back of the tongue?
   a. salty
   b. sweet
   c. sour
   d. bitter

TRUE/FALSE

Indicate whether the statement is true (T) or false (F).

_____ 1. Rotary movement of the eyeball is made possible by six short muscles connecting it to the orbital canal.

_____ 2. Behind the lens occupying the entire eye cavity is the clear, jelly-like fluid called the *vitreous humor*.

_____ 3. The retina has the job of image interpretation.

_____ 4. Responsible for hearing alone, the ear translates sound vibrations via the eighth cranial nerve.

_____ 5. Equalization of air pressure on either side of the eardrum is accomplished by the eustachian tubes.

_____ 6. The three areas of the inner ear are the semicircular canals, vestibule chamber, and cochlea.

_____ 7. Located in the tongue are receptors called *taste buds*.

_____ 8. Receptors located in the upper nasal cavity interpret smell.

_____ 9. Tactile corpuscles are not located on the tongue.

FILL IN THE BLANK

Using words from the list below, fill in the blanks to complete the following statements.

semicircular canals	conjunctivitis
eyelids	hyperopia
glaucoma	tympanic membrane

1. Pink eye is the acute form of _____.

2. _____ cases accounts for about 15 percent of cases of blindness in the United States.

3. The vision impairment occurring with age that reduces the amount of light entering the retina is _____.

4. Maintaining body balance is the responsibility of the _____.

5. Another name for the eardrum is the _____.

6. When comparing the eye to a camera, the _____ are equal to a lens cover.

CHAPTER 25
The Circulatory System

CHAPTER OUTLINE

Review the Chapter Outline. If any content area is unclear, review that area before beginning workbook exercises.

A. Overview of the Circulatory System

B. The Heart

C. Blood Vessels

D. Blood Pressure

E. Pulmonary and Systemic Circulation

F. Blood

G. Homeostasis and Bleeding Control

H. Blood Types

I. The Lymphatic System

J. Common Disorders Associated with the Circulatory System

CHAPTER REVIEW

The following is a summary of the chapter. If any of this material is unclear, review it in the textbook again.

The circulatory system consists of the heart, the blood vessels, the blood, and the structures that make up the lymphatic system. The heart is responsible for the movement of blood through the arterial and vascular systems throughout the body, providing oxygenation and the removal of waste from the entire body, while the lymphatic system, a subsystem of the circulatory system, acts as the body's transportation system. The lymphatic system is also responsible for defending the body against disease-causing agents called *pathogens*.

The circulatory system can malfunction and lead to the following disorders: coronary heart disease, atherosclerosis, arteriosclerosis, myocardial infarction, congestive heart failure, arrhythmia, carditis, thrombophlebitis, varicose veins, anemia, leukemia, aneurysm, cerebrovascular accident, hypertension, and hypotension. Common tests include electrocardiography (ECG), nuclear imaging, ultrasound, radiographs, invasive tests, laboratory tests, and procedures.

STUDY AIDS

To ensure that you have achieved the learning objectives:

1. Define and spell the Terms to Learn in the chapter.

_____

_____

_____

_____

_____

_____

_____

_____

_____

_____

_____

_____

_____

_____

_____

_____

_____

_____

_____

_____

_____

_____

_____

_____

_____

_____

_____

_____

_____

_____

_____

_____

_____

_____

_____

_____

_____

_____

2. Draw and identify the organs of the circulatory system, labeling the structures of the heart and explaining their function.

3. Trace and discuss the conduction system of the heart.

4. Explain the functions of the arteries, veins, and capillaries.

5. Create a chart of the components of blood and explain their functions.

6. Draw plasma and label the substances found in it.

7. Discuss how bleeding is controlled.

8. Distinguish between blood types and between Rh-positive and Rh-negative blood.

9. Discuss the importance of blood typing and cite the blood types that are compatible.

10. Identify the organs of the lymphatic system and cite the location and function of each.

11. Define lymph and explain how it circulates throughout the body.

_____

_____

_____

_____

12. Identify and describe the common disorders associated with the circulatory system.

13. Identify and discuss common diagnostic tests associated with the circulatory system.

MEDICAL TERMINOLOGY REVIEW

Using a dictionary and highlighted terms in the textbook, define the following terms.

Anemia _____

_____

Aneurysm _____

_____

Angioplasty _____

_____

Arrhythmia _____

_____

Arteriosclerosis _____

_____

Atherosclerosis _____

_____

Atria _____

_____

Atrioventricular node _____

_____

Bicuspid valve _____

_____

Bradycardia _____

_____

Bundle of His _____

_____

Congestive heart failure _____

_____

Coronary heart disease _____

● _____

Diastolic blood pressure _____

_____

Dyspnea _____

_____

Endocardium _____

_____

Erythrocytes _____

_____

Heart murmur _____

_____

Hemostasis _____

_____

Hypertension _____

_____

Hypotension _____

_____

Leukemia _____

● kocytes _____

_____

Lymph _____

_____

Myocardial infarction _____

_____

Myocardium _____

_____

Pericardium _____

_____

Platelets _____

_____

Purkinje fibers _____

_____

RhoGAM _____

_____

Sinoatrial node _____

_____

Systolic blood pressure _____

● _____

Tachycardia _____

_____

Thrombophlebitis _____

_____

Tricuspid valve _____

_____

Ventricles _____

_____

SKILL BUILDING

Read and follow the directions below.

Although you will perform tests in a future chapter, role play what you might say to a patient about preparing for laboratory tests related to the cardiovascular system.

CRITICAL THINKING

1. Why is it important to place ECG leads correctly?

_____

_____

_____

_____

2. After a sore throat, a patient finds a lump in a lymph node. Explain what might be happening within the lymph node.

_____

_____

_____

_____

3. Why do you think patients develop anemia?

_____

_____

_____

_____

4. Why should you take a pulse for a full minute?

_____

_____

_____

CHAPTER REVIEW TEST

MULTIPLE CHOICE

Circle the letter of the correct answer.

1. Which blood type is the universal donor?
   a. A
   b. B
   c. AB
   d. O

2. Which blood type is the universal recipient?
   a. A
   b. B
   c. AB
   d. O

3. When taking a pulse, you notice that the pulse slows and speeds up. This patient has
   a. aneurysm
   b. anemia
   c. arrhythmia
   d. angioplasty
   e. atherosclerosis

4. What is another name for red blood cells?
   a. leukocytes
   b. platelets
   c. plasma
   d. erythrocytes
   e. thrombocytes

5. Which of the following is also known as the *pacemaker*?
   a. Purkinje fibers
   b. atrioventricular node
   c. sinoatrial node
   d. bundle of His

6. Which of the following is the name for high blood pressure?
   a. hemostasis
   b. hemorrhage
   c. heart murmur
   d. hypotension
   e. hypertension

7. Which of the following means stoppage of blood?
   a. hemostasis
   b. hemorrhage
   c. heart murmur
   d. hypotension
   e. hypertension

8. Which valve has three parts?
   a. tricuspid
   b. bicuspid
   c. mitral

9. The muscle of the heart is called the
   a. systole
   b. diastole
   c. myocardium
   d. pericardium
   e. endocardium

10. Blood typing is done on
    a. leukocytes
    b. platelets
    c. erythrocytes
    d. thrombocytes
    e. monocytes

TRUE/FALSE

Indicate whether the statement is true (T) or false (F).

_____ 1. Included in the cardiovascular system are the heart, blood, plasma, and blood vessels.

_____ 2. Arteries have thick walls and are larger than veins.

_____ 3. Collecting blood from the lungs and pumping it through the body is the responsibility of the left side of the heart.

_____ 4. Platelets are composed of plaque deposits in the blood.

_____ 5. The ventricular walls are thinner than the atria due to higher pressure.

_____ 6. Autorhythmicity is the unique ability of the cardiac muscles to contract on their own.

_____ 7. The vagus nerves are located in the parasympathetic divisions.

_____ 8. Hormones and body temperature can alter heart rate.

_____ 9. Blood is five times thinner than water.

_____ 10. About 100 different substances are dissolved in plasma.

FILL IN THE BLANK

Using words from the list below, fill in the blanks to complete the following statements.

cardiovascular	myocardial infarct (MI)
blood	leukemia
leukocytes	hemophilia

1. Platelets, _____, erythrocytes, and plasma are the major components of blood.

2. _____ is carried away from the heart by the arteries.

3. A major player in the body's defense against infection is the _____ system.

4. An inherited blood condition that stops or slows blood clotting is known as _____.

5. _____ is blockage of blood flow through the coronary artery, which can starve the heart muscle and cause tissue damage or death.

6. _____, leukocytosis, and leukopenia are all problems involving the white blood cells.

CHAPTER 26

The Immune System

CHAPTER OUTLINE

Review the Chapter Outline. If any content area is unclear, review that area before beginning workbook exercises.

    A.   Anatomy of the Immune System
    B.   The Immune System and the Body's Defense
    C.   Common Disorders Associated with the Immune System

CHAPTER REVIEW

The following is a summary of the chapter. If any of this material is unclear, review it in the textbook again.

The immune system is an amazing protective mechanism consisting of the tissues, organs, and physiologic processes used by the body to identify abnormal cells, foreign substances and tissue, such as transplants, and to defend against those substances that might be harmful to the body. These harmful substances can be bacteria, microbes, viruses, toxins, and parasites. To understand the power of the immune system, consider what happens to a human being who dies. The immune system shuts down, and within hours, the body is invaded by all sorts of bacteria, microbes, and parasites. This invasion causes decomposition of the soft tissue until all that is left is a skeleton.

Several structures are central to the immune system. These include the central lymphoid tissue, which is comprised of the bone marrow and thymus, and the peripheral lymphoid tissue, consisting of the lymph nodes, spleen, and mucosa-associated lymphoid tissue.

Antigens enter the body and cause an antigen-versus-antibody response. Some immunity is innate, active, or passive.

Common disorders of the immune system include allergies, cancer, chronic fatigue syndrome (CFS), infectious mononucleosis, lymphedema, rheumatoid arthritis, and systemic lupus erythrematosis.

STUDY AIDS

To ensure that you have achieved the learning objectives:

1. Define and spell the Terms to Learn in the chapter.

_____

_____

_____

_____

_____

_____

_____

_____

_____

_____

_____

_____

_____

_____

_____

_____

_____

_____

_____

_____

_____

_____

_____

2. Explain the immune system and its response.
3. Identify and discuss the anatomy of the immune system.
4. Discuss the functions of the immune system.
5. List and briefly discuss disorders of the immune system.

_____

_____

_____

_____

_____

MEDICAL TERMINOLOGY REVIEW

Using a dictionary and highlighted terms in the textbook, define the following terms.

Active immunity _____

_____

Antibodies _____

_____

Antigen _____

_____

B lymphocytes _____

_____

Chemotherapy _____

_____

Chronic fatigue syndrome (CFS) _____

_____

Complement _____

_____

Cortex _____

_____

Germinal centers _____

_____

Immune response _____

_____

Immune system _____

_____

Infectious mononucleosis _____

_____

Leukocytes _____

_____

Lymphadema _____

_____

Lymphocytes _____

_____

Medulla _____

_____

Metastasis _____

_____

Neutrophils _____

_____

Oncogenes _____

_____

Phagocytes _____

_____

Radiation therapy _____

_____

Rheumatoid arthritis _____

_____

Systemic lupus erythematosus (SLC) _____

_____

T lymphocytes _____

_____

Trabeculae _____

_____

SKILL BUILDING

Read and follow the directions below.

Role play with a colleague or student the immune system's response to an antigen. One of you should be the antigen and the other the antibody response.

CRITICAL THINKING

1. Stress can weaken the immune system. Why are you more likely to be invaded by a bacterium if you go outdoors with wet hair in cold weather?

   _____

   _____

   _____

2. What types of patients are most vulnerable to invasion by viruses?

   _____

   _____

   _____

3. What are some common environmental elements in your area that cause allergies?

   _____

   _____

   _____

CHAPTER REVIEW TEST

MULTIPLE CHOICE

Circle the letter of the correct answer.

1. Certain people are genetically immune to the bubonic plague. What kind of immunity is this?
   a. innate
   b. acquired
   c. passive

2. Immunity transferred to the infant in breast milk is what type?
   a. innate
   b. acquired
   c. passive

3. Which of the following is NOT part of the immune system?
   a. thyroid
   b. thymus
   c. lymph
   d. tonsils
   e. leukocytes

4. The combining form for cancer is
   a. anti
   b. ante
   c. onco
   d. metasto
   e. cancero

5. The most numerous white blood cell is the
   a. basophil
   b. eosinophil
   c. monocyte
   d. neutrophil
   e. lymphocyte

6. Which of the following is NOT produced in bone marrow?
   a. B cells
   b. natural killer cells
   c. granulocytes
   d. red blood cells
   e. myelin

7. Which of the following diseases is contagious?
   a. cancer
   b. chronic fatigue syndrome
   c. leukemia
   d. mononucleosis
   e. allergy

8. Which of the following therapies involves toxic drugs?
   a. radiation therapy
   b. surgery
   c. chemotherapy
   d. oncogenes

9. Which of the following immune system organs is located in the mediastinum?
   a. spleen
   b. tonsils
   c. appendix
   d. thymus

10. When a foreign substance invades the body, it is called a(n)
   a. anemia
   b. antigen
   c. antibody
   d. oncogene
   e. allergy

11. Which of the following diseases can turn the skin red?
   a. chronic fatigue syndrome (CFS)
   b. infectious mononucleosis
   c. lymphedema
   d. rheumatoid arthritis
   e. systemic lupus erythematosus

TRUE/FALSE

Indicate whether the statement is true (T) or false (F).

_____ 1. Immunity can be innate, passive, or active.

_____ 2. Lymphedema is a common disorder of the immune system.

_____ 3. Mononucleosis is not infectious.

_____ 4. Stress has little or no effect on the immune system.

_____ 5. Lymph nodes are part of the immune system.

_____ 6. Passive and innate immunity are the same.

_____ 7. Rheumatoid arthritis is not a disorder of the immune system.

_____ 8. Bacteria, viruses, microbes, toxins, and parasites are harmful to the body.

_____ 9. The immune system is a proactive mechanism used by the body.

_____ 10. Antigens cause an antigen vs. antibody response.

FILL IN THE BLANK

Using words from the list below, fill in the blanks to complete the following statements.

chemotherapy	physiologic
fatigue	lupus erythematosus
peripheral lymphatic system	immune system
vulnerable	mucosa-associated
tissues	breast milk
organs	antibody

1. Lymph nodes, spleen, and tonsils make up the _____.

2. Immunity works by an antigen versus _____ response.

3. Chronic _____ syndrome is a common immune system response.

4. The immune system consists of _____, _____, and _____ processes.

5. After a person dies, within hours the _____ shuts down.

6. Central lymphoid, peripheral lymphoid, and _____ lymphoid tissue are central to the immune system.

7. Immunity can be transferred to an infant in _____.

8. Patients with weakened immune systems are _____ to viral invasion.

9. _____ is a treatment for cancer.

10. Systemic _____ can turn the patient's skin red.

CHAPTER 27

The Respiratory System

CHAPTER OUTLINE

Review the Chapter Outline. If any content area is unclear, review that area before beginning workbook exercises.

    A. Organs of the Respiratory System

    B. Mechanism of Breathing

    C. Respiratory Volumes and Capacities

    D. Common Disorders Associated with the Respiratory System

CHAPTER REVIEW

The following is a summary of the chapter. If any of this material is unclear, review it in the textbook again.

The primary function of the respiratory system is to provide gas exchange. It does this through respiration, or breathing. When we breathe, we inhale oxygen and exhale carbon dioxide. This exchange of gases is the respiratory system's means of getting oxygen to the blood.

Respiration is achieved through the mouth, nose, trachea, lungs, and diaphragm. Oxygen enters the respiratory system through the mouth and nose. It passes through the larynx (where speech sounds are produced) and then through the trachea, a tube that enters the thoracic cavity. In the chest cavity, the trachea splits into two smaller tubes called *bronchi*. Each bronchus leads directly into the lungs, where it divides again, forming the *bronchial tubes*. The bronchial tubes divide into many smaller tubes called *bronchioles*, connected to tiny sacs called *alveoli*. The average adult's lungs contain about 600 million of these spongy, air-filled sacs that are surrounded by capillaries. These alveoli are the final branchings of the respiratory tree and are the site of gas exchange for the lung. The inhaled oxygen passes into the alveoli and then diffuses through the capillaries into the arterial blood. Meanwhile, the waste-rich blood from the veins releases its carbon dioxide into the alveoli. The carbon dioxide follows the same path out of the lungs when you exhale.

The diaphragm is a sheet of muscles that lies across the bottom of the chest cavity and is the major muscle of respiration. When the diaphragm contracts, it flattens out and allows expansion of the lung tissue, permitting air rich in oxygen to be pulled into the lungs. When the diaphragm relaxes, it returns to its dome shape and forces carbon dioxide out of the lungs.

During the act of breathing, different volumes of air move in and out at different capacities, and these capacities can be calculated by adding specific respiratory volumes together. For example, when measuring lung volume, the following volumes are used:

- Tidal volume (V_T)—volume of air entering or leaving the lungs during a single breath.
- Inspiratory reserve volume (IRV)—volume of air that can be inspired over and above the resting tidal volume.
- Expiratory reserve volume (ERV)—volume of air that can be expired after a normal expiration.
- Residual volume (RV)—volume of air remaining in the lungs after a maximal expiration, which can be estimated as 25 percent of the vital capacity.

When measuring lung capacities, the following measurements are used:

- Inspiratory capacity (IC)—maximum volume that can be inspired after a normal expiration: VT + IRV.
- Vital capacity (VC)—maximum volume that can be expired after a maximal inspiration: VT + IRV + ERV.
- Functional residual capacity (FRC)—volume of air left in the lungs after a normal expiration: ERV + RV.
- Total lung capacity (TLC)—volume of the lungs when fully inflated: VC + RV (or 1.25 × VC).

To determine respiratory volume and capacity, other measurements are often used to calculate ventilation and respiratory capacity. These may include the following:

- Respiratory rate (f)—number of breaths per minute.
- Minute ventilation (V_E)—total volume of air expired per minute: V_T × f.
- Dead space (V_D)—volume of inspired air that is not available for gas exchange.
- Alveolar ventilation (V_A)—volume of air that reaches the alveoli per minute: (V_T − V_D) × f.

Common diseases of the respiratory system include asthma, chronic obstructive pulmonary disease, cystic fibrosis, common cold, hay fever, influenza, Legionnaire's disease, lung cancer, pleurisy, pneumonia, pulmonary edema, pulmonary embolism, severe acute respiratory syndrome, sinusitis, and tuberculosis.

STUDY AIDS

To ensure that you have achieved the learning objectives:

1. Define and spell the Terms to Learn in the chapter.

_____

_____

_____

_____

_____

_____

_____

_____

_____

_____

_____

_____

_____

_____

_____

_____

_____

_____

_____

2. Explain the purpose and function of the respiratory system.

3. List and explain the structures and functions of the organs of the respiratory system.

_____

_____

_____

_____

_____

_____

4. Explain the different respiratory volumes and capacities.

5. Identify and discuss common disorders associated with the respiratory system.

MEDICAL TERMINOLOGY REVIEW

Using a dictionary and highlighted terms in the textbook, define the following terms.

Asthma _____

_____

Atmospheric pressure _____

_____

Bronchitis _____

_____

Chronic obstructive pulmonary disease (COPD) _____

_____

Cilia _____

_____

Common cold _____

_____

Cyanosis _____

_____

Cystic fibrosis (CF) _____

_____

Emphysema _____

_____

Hay fever _____

Hemoptysis _____

Influenza _____

Legionnaire's disease _____

Lung cancer _____

Pleurisy _____

Pneumonia _____

Pulmonary edema _____

Pulmonary embolism (PE) _____

Severe acute respiratory syndrome (SARS) _____

Sinusitis _____

Tuberculosis (TB) _____

SKILL BUILDING

Read and follow the directions below.

Discuss respiratory testing.

CRITICAL THINKING

1. What position should a patient experiencing dyspnea be placed in?

_____

_____

_____

_____

2. How was SARS spread from Asia to North America?

_____

_____

_____

3. How can the medical assistant prevent the transmission of colds or influenza in the medical office?

_____

_____

_____

CHAPTER REVIEW TEST

MULTIPLE CHOICE

Circle the letter of the correct answer.

1. Which of the following means the volume of air that can be expired after a normal expiration?
   a. TLC
   b. ERV
   c. IRV
   d. VT
   e. RV

2. Which of the following means the volume of the lungs when fully inflated?
   a. TLC
   b. ERV
   c. IRV
   d. VT
   e. RV

3. Which of the following is a chronic obstructive pulmonary disease?
   a. pulmonary edema
   b. SARS
   c. cystic fibrosis
   d. influenza
   e. emphysema

4. Which of the following diseases originated in Asia?
   a. Legionnaire's disease
   b. cystic fibrosis
   c. SARS
   d. emphysema
   e. asthma

5. Which of the following is an airborne disease?
   a. cystic fibrosis
   b. emphysema
   c. Legionnaire's disease
   d. cyanosis
   e. pulmonary embolism

6. Which of the following is NOT an airborne disease?
   a. influenza
   b. tuberculosis
   c. Legionnaire's disease
   d. SARS
   e. cystic fibrosis

7. Which of the following means the maximum volume that can be expired after a maximal inspiration?
   a. VC
   b. ERV
   c. IRV
   d. TLC
   e. RV

8. Which are the smallest parts of the respiratory system?
   a. bronchi
   b. trachea
   c. alveoli
   d. pharynx
   e. larynx

9. Which of the following are tiny hairs?
   a. alveoli
   b. cyanosis
   c. cilia
   d. pleurisy
   e. pneumonia

10. What is the sheet of muscles that lies across the bottom of the chest cavity?
    a. pleurisy
    b. cystic fibrosis
    c. diaphragm
    d. bronchi
    e. pectoris majoris

TRUE/FALSE

Indicate whether the statement is true (T) or false (F).

_____ 1. The trachea is not part of the respiratory system.

_____ 2. Cystic fibrosis is a disorder associated with the respiratory system.

_____ 3. Inhalation and perspiration are the mechanisms of breathing.

_____ 4. The pharynx and larynx are the same organ.

_____ 5. Gas exchange is important only to infants or the elderly.

_____ 6. Speech sounds are produced in the larynx.

_____ 7. The diaphragm is not always necessary for breathing.

_____ 8. Lung volume measurements are important for COPD patients.

_____ 9. Dyspnea means "breathing without difficulty."

_____ 10. SARS originated in Asia.

FILL IN THE BLANK

Using words from the list below, fill in the blanks to complete the following statements.

diaphragm	tidal volume
Legionnaire's disease	bronchi
total lung capacity (TLC)	sinusitis
oxygen	transmission
carbon dioxide	cyanosis

1. _____ and _____ are the gases we exchange when we breathe.

2. The _____ is a sheet of muscles that lies across the bottom of the chest cavity

3. _____ is an airborne disease.

4. The volume of the lungs when totally inflated (VC + RV) is the _____.

5. The volume of air leaving or entering the lungs during a single breath is the _____.

6. Inflammation of the sinuses is called _____.

7. Hand washing is the best way to prevent the _____ of colds or influenza.

8. A bluish discoloration of the skin is _____.

9. The trachea splits into two smaller tubes called _____.

10. When the _____ flexes, it forces carbon dioxide out of the lungs.

CHAPTER 28
The Digestive System

CHAPTER OUTLINE

Review the Chapter Outline. If any content area is unclear, review that area before beginning workbook exercises.

    A.   Organs of the Digestive System

    B.   Common Disorders Associated with the Digestive System

CHAPTER REVIEW

The following is a summary of the chapter. If any of this material is unclear, review it in the textbook again.

The digestive system contains those organs that are responsible for getting food into and out of the body and for making use of it. The organs of the digestive system are the mouth, teeth, pharynx, esophagus, stomach, and small and large intestines. Accessory organs include salivary glands, the gallbladder, the liver, and the pancreas. The main part of the digestive system is the digestive tract, a tube, some 30 feet long in adults, through the middle of the body. It starts at the mouth, where food and drink enter the body, and ends at the anus, where leftover food and wastes leave the body. The three main functions of the digestive system are digestion, absorption, and elimination (by means of urine or feces). Common disorders of the digestive system include appendicitis, cirrhosis, colitis, colorectal cancer, constipation, Crohn's disease, diarrhea, diverticulitis, gastroesophageal reflux disease (GERD), hemorrhoids, hernias (hiatal and inguinal), irritable bowel syndrome, oral and pancreatic cancer, peptic ulcer disease, pyloric stenosis, and stomach ulcers.

STUDY AIDS

To ensure that you have achieved the learning objectives:

1. Define and spell the Terms to Learn in the chapter.

_____

_____

_____

_____

_____

_____

_____

_____

_____

_____

_____

_____

_____

_____

_____

_____

_____

_____

_____

_____

2. Describe the purpose and function of the digestive system.

3. Identify the primary organs of the digestive system and briefly explain the function of each.

4. Differentiate between childhood and adult teeth.

5. Draw and label the three main portions of a tooth.

6. Identify the accessory organs of the digestive system and state the function of each.

7. Briefly explain common disorders associated with the digestive system.

MEDICAL TERMINOLOGY REVIEW

Using a dictionary and highlighted terms in the textbook, define the following terms.

Appendicitis _____

_____

Cirrhosis _____

_____

Colitis _____

_____

Colorectal cancer _____

_____

Constipation _____

_____

Crohn's disease _____

_____

Diarrhea _____

_____

Diverticulitis _____

_____

Diverticulosis _____

_____

Gastroesophageal reflux disease (GERD) _____

_____

Hemorrhoid _____

_____

Hernia _____

_____

Hiatal hernia _____

_____

Inguinal hernia _____

_____

Irritable bowel syndrome (IBS) _____

_____

Oral cancer _____

_____

Pancreatic cancer _____

_____

Peptic ulcer disease (PUD) _____

_____

Pyloric stenosis _____

_____

Stomach ulcers _____

_____

SKILL BUILDING

Read and follow the directions below.

Discuss the equipment necessary for rectal exams, sigmoidoscopy, and endoscopy.

CRITICAL THINKING

1. Why is it important to be sure that a patient takes an enema and does not eat after midnight before a bowel x-ray?

   _____

   _____

   _____

   _____

2. Discuss why a sigmoidoscopy might be done in an outpatient clinic but a colonoscopy is usually done in a hospital.

   _____

   _____

   _____

   _____

3. Discuss why a patient with cirrhosis might need smaller dosages of medications.

   _____

   _____

   _____

   _____

CHAPTER REVIEW TEST

MULTIPLE CHOICE

Circle the letter of the correct answer.

1. Which is the organ at the end of the alimentary (digestive) canal?
   a. mouth
   b. stomach
   c. small intestine
   d. anus
   e. appendix

2. Which of the following is the word for gums?
   a. molar
   b. canine
   c. gingiva
   d. anus
   e. appendix

3. Which of the following means stones in the gallbladder?
   a. Crohn's disease
   b. cholelithiasis
   c. pyloric stenosis
   d. irritable bowel syndrome
   e. hemorrhoids

4. Which disorder usually occurs in the anus?
   a. Crohn's disease
   b. cholelithiasis
   c. pyloric stenosis
   d. irritable bowel syndrome
   e. hemorrhoids

5. Which is a disease of the liver?
   a. pyloric stenosis
   b. hemorrhoids
   c. cirrhosis
   d. Crohn's disease
   e. gingivitis

6. Which word means removal of the appendix?
   a. appendicitis
   b. appendotomy
   c. appendectomy
   d. appendices
   e. appendoscopy

Pyloric stenosis occurs in the
   a. esophagus
   b. stomach
   c. small intestine
   d. large intestine
   e. anus

8. Constipation can lead to retention of
   a. chyme
   b. feces
   c. blood
   d. saliva
   e. bile

9. Which organ completes digestion and absorption for the digestive system?
   a. mouth
   b. stomach
   c. small intestine
   d. large intestine
   e. rectum

10. The last adult tooth usually erupts through the gums by age
   a. eight
   b. 14
   c. 18
   d. 21
   e. 30

TRUE/FALSE

Indicate whether the statement is true (T) or false (F).

_____ 1. The tunnel-like structure that contains the organs of the digestive system is the digestive tract.

_____ 2. Mastication is the chewing action used to break down food chemically.

_____ 3. The uvula directs food toward the pharynx and prevents it from exiting through the nose.

_____ 4. The frenulum is responsible for swallowing.

_____ 5. Located under the tongue is the largest of the salivary glands, called the *sublingual gland.*

_____ 6. Holding, tearing, and slashing food are functions of the molars.

_____ 7. The esophagus is responsible for transporting food from the pharynx to the stomach.

_____ 8. The stomach empties about six hours after a meal.

_____ 9. Small in diameter, with a length of about 20 feet, the small intestine is where most food is digested.

_____ 10. The liver performs many functions vital for survival, including detoxification, maintaining body heat, recycling old blood cells, and forming blood plasma protein.

FILL IN THE BLANK

Using words from the list below, fill in the blanks to complete the following statements.

jejunum	diarrhea
gastric juice	rugae
root	colostomy
saliva	pancreas
gastroesophageal reflux disease (GERD)	gallbladder

1. Between 1 and 1.5 liters of _____ are produced each day by the salivary glands.

2. Each tooth has a crown, neck, and _____.

3. When the lower esophageal sphincter does not seal off and allows the acidic stomach contents to reflux into the esophagus, the condition is _____.

4. Another name for the deep folds in the stomach is _____.

5. Mucus, pepsinogen, and hydrochloric acid mix to form _____.

6. The duodenum, the _____, and the ileum are the three regions of the small intestine.

7. When a portion of the colon must be bypassed, a _____ is the procedure used to create a new opening.

8. Located directly under the right lobe of the liver is a sac-shaped organ called the _____.

9. General digestive enzymes excreted by the _____ are carbohydrases, lipases, proteinases, and nucleases.

10. When the fluid contents in the small intestine pass rapidly through the large intestine before adequately absorbing water, the result is _____.

CHAPTER 29
The Urinary System

CHAPTER OUTLINE

Review the Chapter Outline. If any content area is unclear, review that area before beginning workbook exercises.

    A. Organs of the Urinary System

    B. Urine

    C. Common Disorders Associated with the Urinary System

CHAPTER REVIEW

The following is a summary of the chapter. If any of this material is unclear, review it in the textbook again.

The urinary system consists of organs that produce and excrete urine from the body. Urine is a transparent yellow fluid containing unwanted wastes, mostly excess water, salts, and nitrogen compounds. The major organs of the urinary system include the kidneys, a pair of bean-shaped organs that continuously filter substances from the blood and produce urine. Urine flows from the kidneys through two long, thin tubes called *ureters*. With the aid of gravity and wave-like contractions, the ureters transport the urine to the bladder, a muscular vessel. The normal adult bladder can store up to about 0.5 liter (1 pint) of urine before creating a feeling of discomfort or fullness, which it excretes through the tube-like urethra.

In addition to producing and excreting urine from the body, the urinary system is responsible for regulating blood volume and blood pressure by adjusting the volume of water lost in the urine and releasing the hormones erythropoietin and rennin. It is also responsible for regulating the blood concentration of sodium, potassium, chloride, and other ions by controlling the quantities lost in the urine. By doing this, the urinary system conserves valuable nutrients by selectively preventing losses while eliminating waste products.

Organs of the urinary system include the kidneys, ureters, urinary bladder, and urethra. Together they produce and excrete urine.

Common disorders of the urinary system include cystitis, glomerulonephritis, kidney stones, polycystic kidney disease, pyelonephritis, renal failure, and incontinence.

STUDY AIDS

To ensure that you have achieved the learning objectives:

1. Define and spell the Terms to Learn in the chapter.

_____

_____

_____

_____

_____

_____

_____

_____

_____

_____

_____

_____

_____

_____

_____

_____

_____

_____

_____

_____

_____

2. Describe the purpose and function of the urinary system.
3. Identify the organs of the urinary system and briefly explain the function of each.
4. List and discuss the three processes involved in the formation of urine.

_____

_____

_____

_____

_____

_____

5. Explain the normal constituents of urine.

6. List and briefly explain common disorders associated with the urinary system.

_____

_____

_____

_____

_____

_____

MEDICAL TERMINOLOGY REVIEW

Using a dictionary and highlighted terms in the textbook, define the following terms.

Acute renal failure _____

_____

Ascites _____

_____

Chronic renal failure _____

_____

Cortex _____

_____

Cystitis _____

_____

Dialysis _____

_____

Glomerulonephritis _____

_____

Hilum _____

_____

Incontinence _____

_____

Interstitial cystitis (IC) _____

_____

Kidney stones _____

_____

Kidneys _____

_____

Lithotripsy _____

_____

Medulla _____

_____

Nephrons _____

_____

Polycystic kidney disease (PKD) _____

_____

Pyelonephritis _____

_____

Renal calculi _____

_____

Renal pelvis _____

_____

Ureters _____

_____

Urethra _____

_____

Urinary bladder _____

_____

Urinary meatus _____

_____

SKILL BUILDING

Read and follow the directions below.

Role play collecting urine for a sample.

CRITICAL THINKING

1. A patient comes in complaining of great pain and demanding painkillers for a kidney stone. How can you tell if the patient is seeking a drug or has a kidney stone?

   _____

   _____

   _____

   _____

2. You test a patient's urine and find leukocytes, a high glucose level, and ketones. What is probably happening in the patient's body?

   _____

   _____

   _____

   _____

CHAPTER REVIEW TEST

MULTIPLE CHOICE

Circle the letter of the correct answer.

1. Which of the following is the opening to the outside of the body?
   a. ureter
   b. urethra
   c. bladder
   d. meatus
   e. kidney

2. Which of the following is a muscular sac that holds urine?
   a. ureter
   b. urethra
   c. bladder
   d. meatus
   e. kidney

3. For which of the following is there only one organ in the body?
   a. kidney
   b. ureter
   c. urethra

4. Which of the following is used to break up renal calculi?
   a. chemotherapy
   b. radiation therapy
   c. lithotripsy
   d. dialysis
   e. cystoscopy

5. Which of the following terms indicates that the patient cannot control urination?
   a. cystitis
   b. lithotripsy
   c. dialysis
   d. polycystic kidneys
   e. incontinence

6. Which of the following procedures is necessary after renal failure?
   a. radiation therapy
   b. lithotripsy
   c. biopsy
   d. dialysis
   e. chemotherapy

7. Which of the following are fluid-filled sacs?
   a. cysts
   b. nephrons
   c. meatus
   d. renal calculi
   e. ascites

8. Which of the following is a hormone that specifically regulates blood pressure?
   a. prolactin
   b. renin
   c. growth hormone
   d. oxytocin
   e. testosterone

9. Which of the following is about 1½ inches long in the female and about 8 inches long in the male?
   a. kidney
   b. bladder
   c. ureter
   d. urethra
   e. meatus

10. Which of the following is a bladder inflammation?
    a. cystoscope
    b. cystolith
    c. cystotomy
    d. cystectomy
    e. cystitis

TRUE/FALSE

Indicate whether the statement is true (T) or false (F).

_____ 1. Polycystic kidney disease means having more than one kidney.

_____ 2. The urinary system produces and excretes urine from the body.

_____ 3. The adult bladder can hold 2 gallons of urine.

_____ 4. The kidneys, uterus, bladder, and urethra are the organs of the urinary system.

_____ 5. The urinary system regulates the amount of water we excrete in urine, thereby regulating blood volume and blood pressure.

_____ 6. Renal failure is a common disorder of the urinary system.

_____ 7. Kidney stones usually do not cause pain.

_____ 8. High ketone levels will show up in a patient's urine.

_____ 9. Lithotripsy is used to break up renal calculi.

_____ 10. The urinary bladder is a muscular sac.

FILL IN THE BLANK

Using words from the list below, fill in the blanks to complete the following statements.

incontinence	urine
lithotripsy	dialysis
kidneys	uterus
pyelonephritis	urethra
renal calculi	scope
bladder	

1. Renal calculi can be broken up by _____.

2. Cystoscopy involves using a _____ to view the bladder.

3. The bean-shaped organs of the urinary system are the _____.

4. Kidney stones and _____ are the same.

5. Cystitis is inflammation of the _____.

6. _____ is performed on patients in renal failure.

7. Inability to control the flow of urine is _____.

8. The transparent yellow fluid that the urinary system excretes is called _____.

9. The kidneys, _____, urinary bladder, and _____ are the organs of the urinary system.

10. A kidney infection is called _____.

CHAPTER 30
The Endocrine System

CHAPTER OUTLINE

Review the Chapter Outline. If any content area is unclear, review that area before beginning workbook exercises.

    A.   Pituitary Gland

    B.   Pineal Gland

    C.   Thyroid Gland

    D.   Parathyroid Glands

    E.   Pancreas (Islets of Langerhans)

    F.   Adrenal Glands

    G.   Ovaries

    H.   Testes

    I.   Placenta

    J.   Gastrointestinal Mucosa

    K.   Thymus Gland

    L.   Common Disorders Associated with the Endocrine System

CHAPTER REVIEW

The following is a summary of the chapter. If any of this material is unclear, review it in the textbook again.

The endocrine system is made up of hormones and their receptor tissues that regulate secretion via neural/chemical pathways. The primary glands of the endocrine system include the pituitary, or "master gland," pineal, thyroid, parathyroid, pancreas, adrenals, ovaries in the female, and testes in the male.

The vital function of this system is the production and regulation of hormones. Hormones are chemical messengers that regulate body functions including growth, development, mood, tissue function, metabolism, and sexual function in both males and females.

There are many disorders associated with hypersecretion or hyposecretion of hormones of the endocrine system. Controlling the secretion of specific hormones can help treat many of those hormonal conditions or disorders.

The nervous system works closely with the endocrine system to maintain homeostasis. For example, the hypothalamus, which is located in the lower central part of the brain, is the link between the endocrine and nervous systems. The nerve cells in the hypothalamus control the pituitary gland by producing chemicals that suppress or stimulate hormone secretions from the pituitary. The hypothalamus synthesizes and secretes hormones such as thyrotropin-releasing hormone (TRH) and gonadotropin-releasing hormone (GTRH), as well as factors such as corticotropin-releasing hormone (CRF), growth hormone-releasing factor (GHRF), prolactin-releasing factor (PRF), and melanocyte-stimulating releasing factor (MRF). Secretion of the hormones norepinephrine and epinephrine is also controlled by the hypothalamus, which exerts direct nervous control over the anterior pituitary and the adrenal medulla. Disorders associated with the endocrine system include acromegaly, Addison's disease, Cushing's disease, diabetes mellitus, dwarfism, gigantism, hypothyroidism, and hyperthyroidism. Disorders can occur if there is either too much or too little of a hormone.

STUDY AIDS

To ensure that you have achieved the learning objectives:

1. Define and spell the Terms to Learn in the chapter.

_____

_____

_____

_____

_____

_____

_____

_____

_____

_____

_____

_____

_____

_____

_____

_____

_____

2. Describe the primary glands of the endocrine system.
3. State the primary functions of the endocrine glands.
4. Describe the secondary glands of the endocrine system.
5. Explain the vital function of the endocrine glands.
6. Identify and state the functions of the various hormones secreted by the endocrine glands.
7. Identify and explain common disorders of the endocrine system.

MEDICAL TERMINOLOGY REVIEW

Using a dictionary and highlighted terms in the textbook, define the following terms.

Acromegaly _____

_____

Addison's disease _____

Cardiomegaly _____

_____

Cushing's disease _____

Diabetes mellitus _____

_____

Dwarfism _____

_____

Exophthalmos _____

_____

Gestational diabetes _____

_____

Gigantism _____

_____

Goiter _____

_____

Graves' disease _____

_____

Hashimoto's thyroiditis _____

_____

Hyperthyroidism _____

_____

Hypothyroidism _____

_____

Insulin-dependent diabetes mellitus (IDDM) _____

Lipolysis _____

_____

Myxedema _____

_____

Non–insulin-dependent diabetes mellitus (NIDDM) _____

SKILL BUILDING

Read and follow the directions below.

Create a chart that lists the locations of endocrine organs, the hormones they secrete, what each hormone does, and what happens (or what disease occurs) if there is too much or too little of a hormone.

CRITICAL THINKING

1. Why does the endocrine system work very closely with the nervous system?

   _____

   _____

   _____

   _____

2. How does gigantism differ from acromegaly?

   _____

   _____

   _____

   _____

CHAPTER REVIEW TEST

MULTIPLE CHOICE

Circle the letter of the correct answer.

1. Which disease occurs with undersecretion of thyroid hormone?
   a. gigantism
   b. diabetes mellitus
   c. Cushing's disease
   d. Graves' disease
   e. myxedema

2. If a patient has exophthalmos, the diagnosis will probably be
   a. gigantism
   b. diabetes mellitus
   c. Cushing's disease
   d. Graves' disease
   e. myxedema

3. Which of the following is NOT secreted by the thyroid?
   a. T3
   b. T4
   c. calcitonin
   d. prolactin

4. Which of the following is secreted by the testes?
   a. estrogen
   b. progesterone
   c. melatonin
   d. calcitonin
   e. testosterone

5. Which of the following is secreted by the pineal gland?
   a. estrogen
   b. progesterone
   c. melatonin
   d. calcitonin
   e. testosterone

6. Which of the following is the term for diabetes that occurs during pregnancy?
   a. NIDDM
   b. IDDM
   c. gestational diabetes
   d. diabetes insipidus

7. Which disease is caused by hypersecretion of the adrenal glands?
   a. Graves' disease
   b. Cushing's disease
   c. Addison's disease
   d. Hashimoto's thyroiditis
   e. Alzheimer's disease

8. Which of the following is an overgrowth of the extremities?
   a. cardiomegaly
   b. hepatomegaly
   c. acromegaly
   d. carpomegaly
   e. tarsomegaly

9. Undersecretion of growth hormone causes
   a. acromegaly
   b. gigantism
   c. dwarfism
   d. cretinism
   e. cardiomegaly

10. The pituitary gland is controlled by nerve cells in the
    a. adrenal glands
    b. thymus
    c. thyroid
    d. thalamus
    e. hypothalamus

TRUE/FALSE

Indicate whether the statement is true (T) or false (F).

_____ 1. Enlargement of the heart is called *cardiomegaly.*

_____ 2. Gestational diabetes occurs during pregnancy.

_____ 3. Cushing's disease and Graves' disease are nearly the same disorder.

_____ 4. Myxedema means being very confused and swollen.

_____ 5. Hormones are chemical messengers.

_____ 6. PRF is a protein-reactive factor.

_____ 7. Too little or too much of a hormone can cause a disorder of the endocrine system.

_____ 8. The hypothalamus links the nervous and endocrine systems.

_____ 9. The pancreas is the "master gland" of the endocrine system.

_____ 10. Controlling hormone secretion will treat many endocrine disorders.

FILL IN THE BLANK

Using words from the list below, fill in the blanks to complete the following statements.

cortisol	pancreas
adrenal glands	Graves' disease
anterior	hyposecretion
posterior	insulin
hypothalamus	testosterone
acromegaly	

1. The testes secrete which hormone? _____

2. The lobes of the pituitary gland are _____ and _____.

3. _____ is secretion of too little hormone.

4. Hypersecretion of growth hormone in childhood can cause _____.

5. The islets of Langerhans are located in the _____.

6. Exophthalmos is a symptom if _____, a form of hyperthyroidism.

7. Diabetes mellitus is caused by lack of secretion of _____ by the pancreas.

8. Cushing's disease is caused by hypersecretion of _____.

9. The nerve cells in the _____ control the pituitary gland by producing chemicals.

10. The adrenal cortex and adrenal medulla are the _____.

CHAPTER 31
The Reproductive System

CHAPTER OUTLINE

Review the Chapter Outline. If any content area is unclear, review that area before beginning workbook exercises.

    A. Female Reproductive System

    B. The Menstrual Cycle

    C. Male Reproductive System

    D. Common Disorders Associated with the Female Reproductive System

    E. Common Disorders Associated with the Male Reproductive System

CHAPTER REVIEW

The following is a summary of the chapter. If any of this material is unclear, review it in the textbook again.

The reproductive system functions both for reproduction and for maintaining the secondary sex characteristics of both males and females. The female reproductive system is cyclic, with an approximate 28-day cycle as the body prepares itself for reproduction. Female reproductive organs include the uterus, fallopian tubes, ovaries, vagina, vulva, and breast. The male reproductive system produces sperm on a regular basis and does not rely on a cycle for reproduction. The male reproductive system is comprised of the penis, scrotum, testicles, epididymis, vas deferens, prostate, bulbourethral glands, and urethra.

Common disorders associated with the female reproductive system include breast cancer, cervical cancer, cervicitis, dysmenorrhea, endometriosis, fibrocystic breast disease, ovarian cancer, ovarian cysts, pelvic inflammatory disease, premenstrual syndrome, sexually transmitted diseases, uterine cancer, uterine fibroids, and vaginitis. Common disorders affecting the male reproductive system include benign prostatic hyperplasia, epididymitis, erectile dysfunction, and hydrocele. Common procedures include hysterectomy, transurethral resection of the prostate, and vasectomy.

STUDY AIDS

To ensure that you have achieved the learning objectives:

1. Define and spell the Terms to Learn in the chapter.

_____

_____

_____

_____

_____

_____

_____

_____

_____

_____

_____

_____

_____

_____

_____

_____

_____

_____

_____

_____

_____

_____

_____

_____

2. Explain the purpose and function of the female reproductive system.

3. Identify the structures of the female reproductive system and briefly explain the function of each.

4. Describe the menstrual cycle and explain its purpose.

5. Explain the purpose and function of the male reproductive system.

6. Identify the male external organs of reproduction and explain the function of each.

7. Identify and state the function of the testes, epididymis, ductus deferens, seminal vesicles, prostate gland, bulbourethral glands, and urethra.

8. List common disorders associated with the female and male reproductive systems.

_____

_____

_____

_____

_____

_____

_____

_____

_____

MEDICAL TERMINOLOGY REVIEW

Using a dictionary and highlighted terms in the textbook, define the following terms.

Benign prostatic hyperplasia (BPH) _____

_____

Breast cancer _____

_____

Cervical cancer _____

_____

Cervicitis _____

_____

Circumcision _____

_____

Dysmenorrhea _____

_____

Endometriosis _____

_____

Epididymitis _____

_____

Episiotomy _____

_____

Erectile dysfunction (ED) _____

_____

Fibrocystic breast disease _____

_____

Hydrocele _____

_____

Hysterectomy _____

_____

Myomectomy _____

_____

Ovarian cancer _____

_____

Ovarian cysts _____

_____

Ovulation _____

_____

Pelvic inflammatory disease (PID) _____

_____

Perineum _____

_____

Premenstrual syndrome (PMS) _____

_____

Prostate cancer _____

_____

Sexually transmitted infection (STI) _____

_____

Urethritis _____

_____

Uterine cancer _____

_____

Uterine fibroids _____

_____

Vaginitis _____

_____

SKILL BUILDING

Read and follow the directions below.

Using a chart of the reproductive system, identify each organ using the correct medical terminology.

CRITICAL THINKING

1. Why are sexually transmitted diseases so common?

   _____

   _____

   _____

2. Why is a vasectomy an outpatient procedure, whereas a bilateral tubal ligation must be done in a hospital?

   _____

   _____

   _____

3. Is fibrocystic disease cancerous? Explain your answer.

   _____

   _____

   _____

   _____

CHAPTER REVIEW TEST

MULTIPLE CHOICE

Circle the letter of the correct answer.

1. Which of the following is part of the male reproductive system?
   a. vas deferens
   b. fallopian tube
   c. ureter
   d. vulva
   e. clitoris

2. What is the female erectile tissue that is similar to the penis in origin?
   a. vas deferens
   b. fallopian tube
   c. vulva
   d. clitoris
   e. ureter

3. Which of the following is part of the female reproductive system?
   a. vas deferens
   b. epididymis
   c. vulva
   d. urethra
   e. ureter

4. Which of the following is cancerous?
   a. polycystic ovaries
   b. adenocarcinoma of the cervix
   c. cervicitis
   d. fibrocystic disease
   e. pelvic inflammatory disease

5. Which of the following is an overgrowth of an organ?
   a. premenstrual syndrome
   b. benign prostatic hypertrophy
   c. vasectomy
   d. myomectomy
   e. erectile dysfunction

6. What is the name of the disorder in which the patient is unable to achieve or maintain an erection?
   a. premenstrual syndrome
   b. benign prostatic hypertrophy
   c. polycystic disease
   d. erectile dysfunction
   e. epididymitis

7. What is the procedure that removes the foreskin?
   a. hysterectomy
   b. myomectomy
   c. vasectomy
   d. circumcision
   e. episiotomy

8. Which procedure is done to cut the perineum?
   a. hysterectomy
   b. myomectomy
   c. vasectomy
   d. circumcision
   e. episiotomy

9. Painful menstruation is known as
   a. PID
   b. PMS
   c. dysmenorrhea
   d. STD
   e. ED

10. Which of the following describes depressed mood before menstruation?
    a. PID
    b. PMS
    c. dysmenorrhea
    d. STD
    e. ED

TRUE/FALSE

Indicate whether the statement is true (T) or false (F).

_____ 1. The female reproductive cycle is approximately 25 days.

_____ 2. The reproductive system has primarily two functions: reproduction and maintenance of secondary sex characteristics.

_____ 3. Both males and females have a reproductive cycle, but it is much less noticeable in males.

_____ 4. Sexually transmitted diseases affect both males and females.

_____ 5. The fallopian tube carries semen to the penis from the testicles.

_____ 6. Fibrocystic disease is the same as breast cancer.

_____ 7. A circumcision is the procedure that removes the foreskin from the penis.

_____ 8. Paramedics are often referred to as *PMS technicians*.

_____ 9. Often during vaginal childbirth, an episiotomy is performed.

_____ 10. Adenocarcinoma of the cervix is a cancerous condition that should be taken seriously.

FILL IN THE BLANK

Using words from the list below, fill in the blanks to complete the following statements.

fibrocystic   cervical
erectile dysfunction   vulva
menstrual cycle   prostate
hypertrophy   dysmenorrhea
circumcision   premenstrual syndrome
breast

1. _____ and _____ cancer are two common cancers of the female reproductive system.

2. _____ cancer is a potentially serious cancer affecting the male reproductive system.

3. _____ refers to the male's inability to achieve an erection.

4. A lump in the breast could be cancerous or _____ disease.

5. _____ is an overgrowth of an organ.

6. _____ is the procedure that removes the foreskin.

7. The _____ is the clinical term for the vaginal opening.

8. _____ usually results in a painful menstruation cycle.

9. The depressed mood females experience prior to menstruation is called _____.

10. Approximately every 28 days the _____ occurs in females.